W9-CFY-696

PORTALS TO READING

Reading Skills Through Literature

THE TRUMPET
OF THE SWAN

E. B. White

Reproducible Activity Book

The purchase of this book entitles an individual teacher to reproduce pages for use in the classroom. This permitted use of copyrighted material does not extend beyond the building level. Reproduction for use in an entire school system or for commercial use is prohibited. Beyond the classroom use by an individual teacher, reproduction, transmittal, or retrieval of this work is prohibited without written permission from the publisher.

© 1995 Perfection Learning Corporation
1000 North Second Avenue, Logan, Iowa 51546-0500
ISBN-10: 1-5631-2421-1 ISBN-13: 978-1-5631-2421-1

6 7 8 9 10 11 PP 15 14 13 12 11 10

The *Portals to Reading* series accompanies time-tested literature that should be an important part of every school's reading program. The activities will reinforce a wide variety of language and reading skills which are generally part of the curriculum at the reading level of the novel. However, the *Portals* pick-and-choose format gives you the final decision about which activities will enhance your students' personal learning.

The activities in this book are based on sentences and paragraphs especially written to support the teaching objective of each lesson. Clearly, such literary matters as style and flavor may be experienced only by reading the book itself. Thus, the words of the author have been left where they belong—in their pure form in the pages of the novel.

Table of Contents

Word Attack Skills

Comprehension Skills

Study Skills

Creative Skills

Author! Author!
E. B. WHITE

Elwyn Brooks White was born on July 11, 1899, in Mount Vernon, New York. He was the youngest of six children. By the time he was twelve years old, he was the only child still living at home. Later Mr. White explained how this helped him become a writer. As the youngest in a large family, he often felt lonely. So he started writing at an early age.

After graduating from high school, E. B. White went to Cornell University, where he worked on the staff of the school newspaper. As a student, his attention was devoted primarily to the paper and not his classes.

When Mr. White left Cornell, he held a variety of jobs, including work as a news reporter, newspaper columnist, advertising writer, and free-lance writer. In 1927 he was offered a position as a writer for *The New Yorker* magazine. Two years later, he married Katherine Angell, who was an editor on the staff of the magazine.

By 1938 E. B. White and his family had purchased a small farm on the coast of Maine. Although he became increasingly involved in the day-to-day work of running the farm, he still wrote regular columns for *The New Yorker* and *Harper's* magazines, and his wife continued her work as an editor.

E. B. White's first children's book, *Stuart Little*, grew out of stories he told to his son and young nieces and nephews. The book was published in 1945. Seven years later, *Charlotte's Web* was published, much to the delight of young readers everywhere. In 1970 when he was more than seventy years old, E. B. White published *The Trumpet of the Swan.*

On November 1, 1985, E. B. White died.

The Story in Brief

Louis is a trumpeter swan who was hatched on a small pond in Canada. He now lives with his family on the Red Rock Lakes National Wildlife Refuge in Montana. Louis has a wonderful time learning to swim, dive, and fly like his brothers and sisters. But Louis also has a problem—he can't make a single sound. He can't beep, burble, or make the loud echoing call that is the signature of the trumpeter swan. And without a trumpet sound, Louis will be unable to attract Serena, the beautiful swan with whom he has fallen in love.

Louis's father promises to help. So does Sam Beaver, an eleven-year-old boy who loves animals. First Louis goes to school with Sam and learns to read and write. But none of the other swans can read. So although Louis can now communicate with people, he still can't make himself understood to swans. Then Louis's father puts his own honor aside and steals a brass trumpet from a music store. Louis soon learns how to use the instrument to make loud calls just like all of the other swans.

His own problem solved, Louis is determined to pay off his father's debt to the music store. With Sam's help, he gets a job as a bugler at the summer camp for boys. Then Louis travels to Boston, where he is hired to play music for the passengers riding on the Swan Boat in the Public Garden. News of the trumpet-playing swan soon travels to other towns, and Louis is offered a job playing at a nightclub in Philadelphia. In exchange for performing free concerts on Sunday afternoons, he is allowed to live in the Philadelphia Zoo. Louis saves almost all of the money he earns at each job in order to repay his father's debt.

One day a storm blows a strange swan to the shores of the bird pond at the zoo. Louis is thrilled when he realizes that it is Serena, his long-lost love. After Louis's trumpet serenade at dawn, she agrees to be his mate. The two swans return to Red Rock Lakes, and Louis proudly gives his father enough money to pay the music store owner for the cost of the trumpet plus damages. In the spring, Louis and Serena return to the little pond in Canada to settle down in their own nest and get on with the business of raising a family.

In the years that follow, Sam Beaver and his father often return to their camp in Canada. Sam walks to the pond to visit his old friend Louis. And when he listens carefully, Sam can hear the faint sound of a trumpet playing taps just before the sun goes down.

© 1995 Perfection Learning Corporation

Using Short Vowels

Read the words in the word box. Each word contains a short vowel sound. Say the words to yourself and listen for the short vowel sounds. Then read each sentence. Choose a word from the word box to complete each sentence. Write your answer on the blank line.

investigated	sizzling	problem
~~traveling~~	muskrat	pleasant
boggy	intention	trudged
trumpeting	wilderness	

Example: Sam was _____*traveling*_____ in a westward direction.

1. The ground in the swamp was wet and _____.

2. Sam knew it would be easy to get lost in the unsettled _____.

3. As Sam _____ through the swamp, he checked to be sure he was going in the right direction.

4. Sam knew he was close to camp when he smelled _____ fish.

5. Sam told his father he saw a _____ and some birds at the pond.

6. Sam used his compass because he had no _____ of getting lost.

7. Sam's main _____ was deciding what he wanted to be when he grew up.

8. The two swans carefully _____ every part of the pond.

9. The female swan looked for a safe and _____ place to make her nest.

10. The creatures of the swamp could hear the _____ of the huge swans.

© 1995 Perfection Learning Corporation

Finding Base Words

Each word below has been made by adding an ending such as *-ly*, *-ed*, or *-ing* to a base word. On the blank beside each word, write the base word.

Example: glided _____*glide*_____

1. swampy _____

2. bogged _____

3. certainly _____

4. craziest _____

5. discovery _____

6. patches _____

7. warmth _____

8. buried _____

9. trumpeting _____

10. rearing _____

11. circling _____

12. replied _____

13. sandy _____

14. stepped _____

15. nicely _____

16. webbed _____

17. slowly _____

18. grassy _____

19. scooping _____

20. cried _____

© 1995 Perfection Learning Corporation

THE TRUMPET OF THE SWAN

Chapters 1-2

Listening for Syllables

Say each of the words below to yourself. The number of vowel sounds you hear in each word will be the same as the number of syllables. Decide how many syllables are in each word. Then write the number on the blank line after each word.

Example: swamp ___1___

1. eleven	_____		16. flight	_____
2. compass	_____		17. decision	_____
3. Canada	_____		18. grasses	_____
4. enormous	_____		19. ideal	_____
5. cattle	_____		20. location	_____
6. pleasantest	_____		21. enemy	_____
7. female	_____		22. nesting	_____
8. seldom	_____		23. animals	_____
9. heard	_____		24. clout	_____
10. chickadee	_____		25. pretended	_____
11. tomorrow	_____		26. courage	_____
12. creature	_____		27. floated	_____
13. swiftly	_____		28. coarse	_____
14. powerful	_____		29. eagle	_____
15. trumpeting	_____		30. task	_____

© 1995 Perfection Learning Corporation

Making Compounds

Two words combined form a compound. Each word in Box A forms the first part of a compound. Each word in Box B forms the second part. In the blank in each sentence below, write the compound that best completes the sentence. Use a word from each box to make your compounds.

Box A	
after	under
sun	shoe
high	an
~~hide~~	spell
black	note
master	

Box B	
piece	other
birds	water
bound	~~away~~
noon	book
lace	way
light	

Example: The swans hoped for some privacy in their wilderness _____*hideaway*_____.

1. The cob couldn't understand how Sam arrived at a pond that was fifty miles from any _____.

2. Sam was _____ at the sight of the magnificent birds.

3. The cob told his wife that her last egg was a real _____.

4. The swan noticed that the baby _____ had already hatched.

(continued)

© 1995 Perfection Learning Corporation

Making Compounds

Chapters 3-4

5. The warm _____ sun made the female swan feel hot and thirsty.

6. The swan stuck her head _____ and began to drink.

7. Just in case the fox didn't leave, Sam grabbed _____ stick.

8. Every night before going to sleep, Sam wrote in his _____.

9. The cob welcomed his children to the bright _____ of the pond.

10. One of the cygnets pulled Sam's _____ and untied it.

© 1995 Perfection Learning Corporation

Chapters 3-4

Using Long Vowels

Read the words in the word box. Each word contains a long vowel sound. Say the words to yourself and listen for the long vowel sounds. Then read each sentence. Choose a word from the word box to complete each sentence. Write your answer on the blank line.

triumph	gazed	file
breathe	grateful	slight
female	behaving	~~floating~~
creatures	glided	

Example: The two swans were _____*floating*_____ on the water.

1. Searching for enemies, the female swan _____ intently at the point of land.

2. The swans were surprised to see a boy who was _____ himself instead of throwing sticks.

3. Sam loved to sit and watch the wild _____ that lived in the woods.

4. As the _____ swan left the nest, she looked back at her egg.

5. The swans _____ gracefully through the water.

6. The cob was _____ to Sam for saving the female swan's life.

7. The swans' trumpeting voices told of their _____ over the fox.

8. The swan felt a _____ movement and knew the cygnets were beginning to hatch.

9. After hatching out of the cramped egg, the tiny cygnet was glad to _____ the fresh air.

10. The cygnets swam in single _____, with the cob in front and their mother at the rear.

© 1995 Perfection Learning Corporation

Adding Endings

Read each sentence. Then look at the word shown in parentheses at the end of the sentence. Add an ending such as -ed, -ing, -s, or -er to the word to make it fit in the sentence. Remember, you may need to change the word when you add the ending. Write the new word in the blank.

Example: The swan was going to strike Sam with its _____*powerful*_____ wings.   (power)

1. Sam sat and _____ the swans for more than an hour.   (watch)

2. The female swan looked _____ at her five eggs.   (proud)

3. The swan took a bath by _____ water all over herself.   (toss)

4. The swans filled the air with sounds of their _____.   (glad)

5. The swan was grateful to see that her baby was _____.   (health)

6. Sam approached the pond _____.   (cautious)

7. The cob wondered if he looked _____ when seen through field glasses.   (large)

8. Soon Sam saw a tiny head _____ its way out from under the female swan.   (thrust)

9. The most _____ cygnet left the nest first.   (dare)

10. Each cygnet dipped up a small _____ of water.   (mouth)

Classifying Word Groups

Read the following sentences. Decide if the italicized part of the sentence tells you *where*, *when*, or *how*. Underline the correct choice.

Example: *One evening*, the swan told the cob she wanted to talk about Louis.   where   <u>when</u>   how

1. As the swan talked, the cob began to look *worried*.   where   when   how

2. The swan and the cob had met *in Montana*.   where   when   how

3. Louis was growing well and swimming *beautifully*.   where   when   how

4. The swan reminded the cob of the spring, *years ago*, when they had first met.   where   when   how

5. Louis's parents agreed that they needed to watch him *next winter*.   where   when   how

6. The cob couldn't sleep at all *that night*.   where   when   how

7. The cob asked Louis to follow him *to the other end of the pond*.   where   when   how

8. The cob began to speak *candidly and openly* to Louis.   where   when   how

9. *While his father watched*, Louis tried to make a noise.   where   when   how

10. Finally, Louis gave up and hung his head *sadly*.   where   when   how

(continued)

© 1995 Perfection Learning Corporation

Classifying Word Groups

Chapters 5-6

11. The cob's voice was *comforting* as he spoke
    to Louis.   where   when   how

12. The cob promised that *someday* he would help
    Louis find a voice.   where   when   how

13. *At the end of the summer*, the cob gathered his
    children around him.   where   when   how

14. *Soon* Louis and his father joined the rest of
    the family.   where   when   how

15. The Red Rock Lakes are located *in a lovely valley*.   where   when   how

16. Warm water *from hidden springs* made the lakes
    a pleasant place to spend the winter.   where   when   how

17. The cob's wings were beating *strongly and regularly*.   where   when   how

18. Louis splashed water *in his father's face*.   where   when   how

19. The mist rose *from the pond*.   where   when   how

20. Mr. Beaver told Sam they had to leave *tomorrow*.   where   when   how

© 1995 Perfection Learning Corporation

Matching Synonyms

<table>
<tr><td>upset</td><td>show</td><td>ordered</td></tr>
<tr><td>noise</td><td>feeling</td><td>without</td></tr>
<tr><td>meeting</td><td>~~pretty~~</td><td>smart</td></tr>
<tr><td>forces</td><td>place</td><td></td></tr>
</table>

A synonym is a word having the same or nearly the same meaning as another word. Read each sentence. Choose a synonym from the word box to replace the italicized word.

Example: _____*pretty*_____ The cob remembered how *attractive* the swan had seemed to him when he first met her.

_____ 1. Louis's mother knew Louis was *bright* and healthy.

_____ 2. The idea that Louis was defective *distressed* the cob.

_____ 3. Louis was defective because he was *lacking* a voice.

_____ 4. The cob took Louis aside so they could have a quiet, uninterrupted *conference*.

_____ 5. The cob wanted to hear Louis's voice and *commanded* him to make a loud noise.

_____ 6. Louis's father said that not being able to speak *compels* someone to be a good listener.

_____ 7. A swan usually leaves its nesting *site* at the end of summer.

_____ 8. The cygnets watched carefully as their father prepared to *demonstrate* how to fly.

_____ 9. The cob's beating wings and racing feet created a huge *commotion*.

_____ 10. Louis felt a tremendous *sensation* of relief when he realized that he could fly.

© 1995 Perfection Learning Corporation

Remembering Details

The following questions are about the main character and some of the events in the book. Write the answers on the lines below the questions. Be sure to use complete sentences.

1. Why did Louis decide to visit Sam Beaver? _____

   _____

2. When Louis got to a town, why was he afraid to walk down the main street? _____

   _____

3. How did Louis let Sam know who he was? _____

   _____

4. Why did Mr. Beaver call the game warden? _____

   _____

5. Why did Mrs. Beaver make Louis sleep in the barn? _____

   _____

6. How did Mrs. Hammerbotham find out what Louis's name was? _____

   _____

7. Why did Mrs. Hammerbotham have Louis write some words on the board? _____

   _____

Determining Fact and Opinion

Some of the following sentences are statements of fact. Some are statements of opinion. In the blank before each sentence, write the letter *F* if that sentence is a statement of fact. Write *O* if that sentence is a statement of opinion.

Example: ___*O*___ Animals without voices should learn to read and write.

_____ 1. The waters of the Red Rock Lakes stay warm in winter.

_____ 2. It is hard to learn how to read.

_____ 3. Sam was more trustworthy than most boys his age.

_____ 4. Only people need to be able to communicate with one another.

_____ 5. It's against the law to keep some wild animals in captivity.

_____ 6. Trumpeter swans are the most beautiful birds alive.

_____ 7. A young trumpeter swan is a dirty gray color.

_____ 8. The word *catastrophe* is longer than the word *cat*.

_____ 9. Not having a voice is a catastrophe.

_____ 10. Sam was in fifth grade.

© 1995 Perfection Learning Corporation

Matching Antonyms

An antonym is a word that means the opposite or nearly the opposite of another word. Read each sentence. Choose an antonym from the word box to replace the italicized word.

left	weak	success
presence	elderly	perfect
typical	~~ugly~~	male
lot	happily	

Example: _____*ugly*_____ The Red Rock Lakes were an *attractive* and pleasant place to spend the winter.

_____ 1. His family couldn't read what Louis wrote, so his greeting was a *failure*.

_____ 2. Louis's family missed him during his long *absence* from home.

_____ 3. Louis was *defective* because he was born without the ability to speak.

_____ 4. Realizing no one could read his words, Louis *sorrowfully* erased the slate.

_____ 5. Serena was a young *female* swan who lived on the same lake as Louis and his family.

_____ 6. Serena was just a *trifle* smaller than the other female swans.

_____ 7. Louis had strong and *powerful* wings.

_____ 8. Everyone in Billings bought a paper to read about the *extraordinary* actions of the huge swan.

_____ 9. The old cob *returned* home with the trumpet in his beak.

_____ 10. The *youthful* swans were ready to settle down and look for mates.

Name _____

Evaluating What You Read

Read each of the story situations below. Decide whether you agree or disagree with what the character said, did, or thought about the situation. Then explain why you feel as you do.

1. When Louis leaves to learn how to read and write, his family doesn't know where he has gone. The cob isn't sure whether or not he should try to find Louis. He really doesn't want to leave the lakes with winter so near. Then Louis's mother reminds the cob that they have no idea which way Louis went. They decide that there is no sense in trying to find Louis. They will just wait and hope that he returns. Do you agree or disagree with the cob and the swan that there is no use in looking for Louis?

   I _____ with the cob and the swan because _____

   _____

   _____

2. When Louis tries to attract Serena's attention, the young female just ignores him. Serena is curious about Louis, but she doesn't want anything to do with a swan that can't trumpet. Do you agree or disagree with Serena that she shouldn't show any interest in a mate that can't make any noise?

   I _____ with Serena because _____

   _____

   _____

3. The cob feels guilty when he breaks the store window and steals a trumpet. He wonders why he has suddenly become a criminal. Then he decides that even though what he did is wrong, he had to do it to help his son. Do you agree or disagree with the cob that he had to steal a trumpet in order to help Louis?

   I _____ with the cob because _____

   _____

   _____

© 1995 Perfection Learning Corporation

Determining Cause and Effect

To determine a cause, ask "What is the reason?" To determine an effect, ask "What is the result?" Match the causes and effects below. Write the number of the cause in front of its effect.

Cause	**Effect**
1. Louis's parents didn't know which way he had gone.	_____ The cob and the swan were happy to see Louis.
2. Louis returned to the lake and found his parents.	_____ Louis realized that writing would be useful when dealing with people.
3. Louis had been gone for eighteen months.	_____ Louis's dirty gray feathers had changed to the white feathers of an adult swan.
4. The other swans didn't know how to read.	_____ They decided to wait for Louis to return home on his own.
5. The grain man was able to read what Louis wrote.	_____ Louis's writing meant nothing to his family.

Cause	**Effect**
1. Louis's heart beat faster every time he saw Serena.	_____ Serena just stared at the words on the slate and then swam off.
2. Louis wanted to get Serena's attention.	_____ Louis was sure he was in love.
3. Serena didn't know how to read.	_____ He swam around her and pumped his neck up and down.
4. Louis's mother knew that Louis was in love.	_____ The cob decided to find a trumpet for Louis.
5. Louis's mother told the cob that Serena was ignoring their son.	_____ She hid in the bushes to see what happened when Louis tried to get Serena's attention.

© 1995 Perfection Learning Corporation

THE TRUMPET OF THE SWAN

Remembering Details

The following questions are about the main character and some of the events in the book. Write the answers on the lines below the questions. Be sure to use complete sentences.

1. Why did the young female swans notice Louis? _____

   _____

2. Why was Louis finding it more and more difficult to fly? _____

   _____

3. Why did Louis decide to go to see Sam Beaver again? _____

   _____

4. How did Sam help Louis learn to play the trumpet? _____

   _____

5. For his job at the camp, when did Louis have to play the trumpet? _____

   _____

6. How much was Louis going to be paid for working at Camp Kookooskoos? _____

   _____

7. What was Mr. Brickle's explanation for Camp Kookooskoos' strange name ? _____

   _____

© 1995 Perfection Learning Corporation

Discovering Meaning Through Context

Read the following sentences. Three meanings are given for each italicized word. Use the context of the sentence to figure out which meaning is correct. Underline the correct meaning.

Example: Louis kept trying until he was able to make the trumpet *emit* a sound.

        lose   <u>send out</u>   practice

1. Louis found it harder to fly with so many *possessions* hanging from his neck.

        slates   feathers   belongings

2. At night, when the light *faded* in the sky, it was time to play taps.

        grew dim   fell   grew bright

3. Sam sat in the *stern* of the boat and put Louis in front where he could see him.

        top   back   seat

4. Sam's canoe *grounded* on the sandy beach near the camp.

        got muddy   sank   touched shore

5. Everyone crowded so close to Louis that he was almost *crushed.*

        happy   ignored   squashed

(continued)

Discovering Meaning
Through Context

Chapters 10-11

6. Sam was worried and *implored* the campers to be careful not to hurt Louis.

   begged   wrote   showed

7. The boys sat around the fire and *swatted* the mosquitoes that were trying to bite them.

   burned   hit   looked at

8. Every evening, Louis would play taps to bring the day's activities to a *close*.

   counselor   sad note   end

9. Mr. Brickle told the boys that a *peculiar* name made a camp seem interesting and unusual.

   short   strange   dull

10. The last note of taps seemed to *linger* in the air for hours.

   stay   disappear   fall apart

© 1995 Perfection Learning Corporation

Using Cloze Reading

Read the paragraphs below. Use the words in the word box to fill in the blanks. The first example is done for you.

noise	trumpeter	positions
summer	trying	tongue
clear	cheeks	~~trumpet~~
beat	listen	

Louis was delighted to have a (1) _____*trumpet*_____, but he soon discovered that it

wasn't easy to make a (2) _____ with the instrument. He tried holding the

trumpet in several different (3) _____, but no sound came out. He blew

hard and puffed out his (4) _____, but still nothing happened.

Eventually Louis found that he could make a sound by holding his (5) _____

a certain way while blowing into the trumpet. At first the noise wasn't very pretty, but Louis

kept (6) _____. On the second day of practice, he finally got the trumpet to

play a (7) _____ note. Louis's heart skipped a (8) _____ at

the sound. A duck stopped to (9) _____ to the unusual noise. Louis was

determined to become a great (10) _____. He decided to practice blowing

the horn all (11) _____ long if necessary.

Getting the Main Idea

Read each of the following paragraphs. Then read the four sentences below each paragraph. Choose the sentence that best states the main idea of the paragraph. Then neatly copy that sentence on the line provided.

a. Louis was an excellent volleyball player. With his long neck he could reach the ball easily and hit it over the net. At the nightly volleyball games, all the boys wanted to be on Louis's team.

1. Louis had a long neck.
2. Louis hit the ball over the net.
3. Louis was good at volleyball.
4. Louis played volleyball every night.

b. Louis heard Applegate calling for help. Quickly, the swan dropped everything and splashed into the water. His powerful wings and feet carried him to the struggling boy. Louis dove down and came up underneath Applegate. The boy hung on to Louis's neck as the swan carried him to safety.

1. Louis had powerful wings and feet.
2. Louis saved Applegate from drowning.
3. Applegate hung on to Louis.
4. Louis dropped his things before getting into the water.

(continued)

© 1995 Perfection Learning Corporation

Getting the Main Idea

Chapters 12-13

c.   Louis wanted to be able to play all sorts of music. But his webbed feet made it impossible for him to use the valves on the trumpet. Louis asked Sam to slit the web on his right foot. After Sam slit the web, Louis could move his toes independently. He could play all the notes on the trumpet!

1. Louis's trumpet had valves that Louis couldn't use.
2. Louis had webbed feet.
3. Louis asked Sam to help him.
4. Louis wanted his web slit so he could play all kinds of music.

---

d.   Louis had many important possessions. Even though they made it harder to fly, he knew he had to have all of his things with him. He needed his trumpet to make noise. He needed his moneybag to hold his money. And he needed his slate and chalk pencil to communicate with people.

1. Louis needed all of his possessions.
2. Louis used his chalk pencil to write on his slate.
3. It was hard for Louis to fly with things hung around his neck.
4. Louis kept his money in his moneybag.

Sequencing Events

The two sets of events listed below are arranged in incorrect sequence. Number each set of events in order from 1 to 5 by writing a *1* in the blank before the event that happened first, a *2* before the event that happened next, and so on.

Set 1

_____ At the end of the day, Louis played taps.

_____ He hid his belongings under a bush.

_____ Near the shore, Louis removed his slate, pencil, and trumpet.

_____ Then he went into the water to sleep.

_____ After taps, Louis waddled down to the beach.

Set 2

_____ When rest period was over, Applegate went to the dock.

_____ The canoe tipped over and Applegate fell into the water.

_____ During rest period, the boys all teased Applegate.

_____ His wet clothes started to pull Applegate under the water.

_____ He got into a canoe and paddled out all by himself.

© 1995 Perfection Learning Corporation

THE TRUMPET OF THE SWAN

Classifying Words

In each group of words below, one word does not belong with the others. Draw a line through the word that does not belong. Then decide what the other three words have in common. Write your answer on the blank line after the words.

Example: boy   girl   ~~trumpet~~   man

They are all *people* _____.

1. Montana   Boston   Ontario   Serena

   They are all _____.

2. watercress   lake   river   stream

   They are all _____.

3. twenty-five   double   fifteen   eleven

   They are all _____.

4. trumpet   moneybag   slate   boat

   They are all _____.

5. hotel   house   garden   store

   They are all _____.

(continued)

Classifying Words

Chapter 14-15

6. dresser   tickets   table   chair

They are all _____.

7. squirrels   pigeons   ducks   swans

They are all _____.

8. napkin   spoon   knife   fork

They are all _____.

9. toilet   tub   shower   desk

They are all _____.

10. waiter   desk clerk   boatman   bellboy

They are all _____.

© 1995 Perfection Learning Corporation

Making Inferences

Read each of the questions below. Then read the three possible answers. Think about what happened in chapters 14 and 15 of *The Trumpet of the Swan*. Use what you know to choose the best answer for each question. Circle the number next to the answer you choose.

a.   Why was the boatman so happy to have Louis playing the trumpet for him?

1. The boatman liked swans.
2. The boatman wanted to help Louis get out of debt.
3. Louis was helping the boatman earn lots of money.

b.   Why was the hotel desk clerk unwilling to give Louis a room?

1. Birds don't usually stay in hotels.
2. Louis didn't have enough money to pay for a room.
3. The desk clerk didn't like swans.

c.   When the girls asked Louis for his autograph, why did the desk clerk think he might have to give the swan a room?

1. The desk clerk realized that Louis must be famous.
2. The desk clerk knew the girls were important hotel guests.
3. The desk clerk wanted to get Louis's autograph too.

(continued)

Name _____

d. Why did Louis order one sandwich with mayonnaise and eleven without?

1. Louis didn't plan on eating all the sandwiches.
2. Louis wanted to have plenty to eat if he found out he didn't like mayonnaise.
3. Louis wasn't really very hungry.

e. Why did the front desk call and tell Louis he couldn't play the trumpet in his room?

1. Louis was a swan, not a human.
2. Someone complained about the noise.
3. Louis didn't play the trumpet very well.

© 1995 Perfection Learning Corporation

Choosing Correct Meanings

The italicized word in each of the sentences below has several meanings. Some of the meanings are listed in the Glossary. Decide which meaning the word has in the sentence. Then write the number of your choice on the blank.

Glossary

bill   1. beak 2. amount owed 3. piece of paper money 4. statement of charges

date   1. day and time 2. kind of fruit 3. appointment for a set time

mind   1. part of the body responsible for thought 2. to obey 3. to dislike

park   1. to leave a car or other vehicle in place 2. enclosed area of land set aside for recreation and enjoyment

safe   1. free from danger 2. place in which valuables can be stored

spring   1. season of the year 2. to jump up 3. water from the ground

Example: _4_   The waiter handed Louis a *bill* for the food.

_____   1. The sign showed the *date* of Louis's first concert.

_____   2. Louis had always been careful to *mind* his mother and father.

_____   3. The Red Rock Lakes were warmed by water from an underground *spring*.

_____   4. Louis took a dollar *bill* out of his moneybag.

_____   5. Louis liked living in the *park* in Boston.

_____   6. Louis made a *date* to meet Mr. Lucas at the zoo.

(continued)

Choosing Correct Meanings

Chapters 16-17

_____ 7. The boatman paid the *bill* for Louis's hotel stay.

_____ 8. Some guests kept their belongings in the hotel *safe*.

_____ 9. Louis saw Mr. Lucas *spring* up from the bench in excitement.

_____ 10. Thoughts of love filled Louis's *mind*.

_____ 11. Swans usually choose their mates in the *spring*.

_____ 12. Louis picked up his slate with his *bill*.

_____ 13. Louis didn't *mind* the Sunday concerts, but he hated working in the nightclub.

_____ 14. Louis watched over his moneybag to be sure it was *safe*.

_____ 15. The taxi driver tried to *park* near the nightclub.

© 1995 Perfection Learning Corporation

THE TRUMPET OF THE SWAN

Making an Outline

Read the article below. Think about the topics and subtopics of each paragraph. Use the Word List provided to outline the article. The topics should come after the numerals. The subtopics come after the capital letters. List the topics and subtopics in the order the items fall in the article.

Part of the outline has been done for you. Be sure to capitalize the first letter of the topics and subtopics.

<hr>

Trumpeter Swans

Trumpeter swans are just one of seven different species of swans. All swans are water birds. They have flattened bills, long necks, water-repellent feathers, long wings, short tails and legs, and webbed feet.

Trumpeter swans are found in North America. They are known for their trumpet-like call. Like other swans of northern regions, trumpeter swans are completely covered with white feathers. The trumpeter swan is the largest species of swan, and an adult male can weigh 26 pounds.

Swans have strong family ties. They choose mates when they are two or three years old, and they usually mate for life. Young trumpeters, called *cygnets*, may stay with their parents until the time comes to choose a mate.

(continued)

Name _____

Word List

_____ _Trumpeter Swans_ _____

I. _____

    A. _____

    B. _____

    C. _Long necks and wings_ _____

    D. _____

    E. _____

II. _Characteristics of trumpeter swans_

    A. _____

    B. _____

    C. _____

    D. _____

III. _____

    A. _Strong family ties_ _____

    B. _____

    C. _____

    D. _____

Water birds

Found in North America

~~Long necks and wings~~

Largest swan

Mate for life

~~Trumpeter Swans~~

Short tails and legs

Babies called _cygnets_

Swan families

Flattened bills

~~Strong family ties~~

Cygnets stay with parents

~~Characteristics~~

Trumpet-like call

All white feathers

Water-repellent feathers

~~Characteristics of trumpeter swans~~

© 1995 Perfection Learning Corporation

Using Guide Words

At the top of each dictionary page are guide words. These words are the first and last words on a dictionary page. The other words on the page fall in alphabetical order between the guide words.

Put the words in the word box in alphabetical order under the correct guide words. The first one has been done for you.

lake	passengers	duck
concerts	sweet	heart
rifle	public	works
hope	farewell	played
place	~~afternoons~~	ping
shiny	honor	hauled

able—hid	**hide—plain**	**plate—wrote**
1. _afternoons_	1. _____	1. _____
2. _____	2. _____	2. _____
3. _____	3. _____	3. _____
4. _____	4. _____	4. _____
5. _____	5. _____	5. _____
6. _____	6. _____	6. _____

© 1995 Perfection Learning Corporation

Using a Pronunciation Key

Use the key at the bottom of the page to help pronounce the respelled words. Write the word correctly spelled on the line beside the Respelled Word. Use the Word List to help figure out the Respelled Word.

Respelled Word		Word List
Example: (pē′ pəl)	*people*	vanished
1. (ak′ səd ənt)	_____	breeze
2. (pin′ yənd)	_____	pain
3. (brēz)	_____	amputated
4. (pō′ əm)	_____	attack
5. (van′ isht)	_____	premiums
6. (ə tak′)	_____	valuable
7. (bil′ dingz)	_____	bayou
8. (pān)	_____	~~people~~
9. (val′ yə [wə] bəl)	_____	cygnets
10. (siv ə lə zā′ shən)	_____	accident
11. (am′ pyə tāt əd)	_____	buildings
12. (prē′ mē əmz)	_____	civilization
13. (sig′ nətz)	_____	pinioned
14. (bī′ [y]ō)	_____	poem

pat/ cāke/ cär/ pet/ mē/ it/ nīce/ pot/ cōld/ nôrth/

book/ fo͞ol/ boil/ out/ cup/ mūle/ burn/ sing/ thin/

*th*is/ hw in **wh**ite/ zh in plea**s**ure/ ə in **a**bout

The ′ mark indicates an accented syllable.

© 1995 Perfection Learning Corporation

Determining Alphabetical Order

Words are listed in a dictionary in alphabetical order. Number the six words in each list below to show the order in which they would appear in the dictionary. Write a *1* in the blank before the word that comes first alphabetically, and so on.

Example:

_2_	delighted
_5_	dreaming
_4_	doubled
_3_	door
_1_	day
_6_	dreamy

A.

_____	handle
_____	horrible
_____	head
_____	high
_____	hardly
_____	hit

B.

_____	arrival
_____	action
_____	air
_____	away
_____	arrived
_____	any

C.

_____	right
_____	raised
_____	reason
_____	rare
_____	realize
_____	raise

D.

_____	slate
_____	sneaking
_____	shot
_____	safety
_____	spring
_____	shotgun

E.

_____	telegram
_____	trumpet
_____	though
_____	thanked
_____	time
_____	thousand

F.

_____	concerts
_____	cygnets
_____	cob
_____	coins
_____	clean
_____	comb

G.

_____	favors
_____	freedom
_____	few
_____	free
_____	fourteen
_____	freer

H.

_____	event
_____	existence
_____	eager
_____	easier
_____	explore
_____	every

© 1995 Perfection Learning Corporation

Using Descriptive Words

List four words that can be used to describe each of the italicized words below. Write your words on the blanks. Be creative.

Example: *ghost*

1. *pale*
2. *spooky*
3. *mischievous*
4. *floating*

A. *fence*

1. _____
2. _____
3. _____
4. _____

B. *lake*

1. _____
2. _____
3. _____
4. _____

C. *swan*

1. _____
2. _____
3. _____
4. _____

D. *zoo*

1. _____
2. _____
3. _____
4. _____

E. *music*

1. _____
2. _____
3. _____
4. _____

F. *plane*

1. _____
2. _____
3. _____
4. _____

© 1995 Perfection Learning Corporation

Recalling an Event

Think about the cob's return to the music store to repay his debt. Then describe this event to someone who has not read the book. Remember to include details about the setting, why the cob was returning to the store, how the cob and the storekeeper felt about the event, and so on.

_____

_____

_____

_____

_____

_____

_____

_____

_____

_____

_____

_____

_____

_____

_____

_____

Writing a Journal Sample

Imagine that you are Sam Beaver. In the sample journal below, pretend that you are writing in your diary about your visit to the Philadelphia Zoo. Explain your feelings about the zoo, your plans for the future, or your reasons for fighting for Serena's freedom.

© 1995 Perfection Learning Corporation

Creating a Character

Imagine that you are a resident of Philadelphia. You have heard Louis's concerts at the zoo and have visited the nightclub to hear him play. Now Louis has left Philadelphia and you're being interviewed by a newspaper reporter. Write your answers to the reporter's questions on the lines provided.

Reporter: What was your reaction the first time you heard Louis play?

Your Answer: _____

_____

Reporter: Did you enjoy Louis's music more at the zoo or at the nightclub? Why?

Your Answer: _____

_____

Reporter: How did you feel when Louis and Serena left Philadelphia?

Your Answer: _____

_____

Reporter: Do you think the head of the zoo was correct to let Serena go free or should he have pinioned her wings so she couldn't leave the zoo? Why do you feel as you do?

Your Answer: _____

_____

Reporter: How do you feel about Louis's promise to donate some of his cygnets to the zoo?

Your Answer: _____

_____

Writing a Book Recommendation

Do you think other students would enjoy reading *The Trumpet of the Swan?* On the lines below, explain why you would recommend reading the book. Mention specific things you liked about the story. For example, did you enjoy the combination of fantasy and fact? Did you think the human characters were realistic? Did the book teach you anything about trumpeter swans? If you didn't like the book, tell why you would not recommend it.

_____

_____

_____

_____

_____

_____

_____

_____

_____

_____

_____

_____

_____

_____

_____

© 1995 Perfection Learning Corporation

Explaining Feelings

The questions below ask you to describe the feelings you had as you read the book. Read each question carefully. Write your response on the lines provided. Explain why you felt the way you did. Be sure to use complete sentences.

1. How did you feel when the cob brought the cygnets to meet Sam?

   _____

   _____

   _____

2. How did you feel when you realized that not having a voice was a problem for Louis?

   _____

   _____

   _____

3. How did you feel when Louis realized that learning to write wasn't going to help him communicate with his family?

   _____

   _____

   _____

(continued)

© 1995 Perfection Learning Corporation

Explaining Feelings

4. How did you feel when the cob stole the trumpet for Louis?

    _____

    _____

    _____

5. How did you feel when Serena fell in love with Louis?

    _____

    _____

    _____

6. How did you feel when Louis promised to donate some of his cygnets to the zoo in exchange for Serena's freedom?

    _____

    _____

    _____

7. How did you feel when the cob returned to the music store with the money?

    _____

    _____

    _____

© 1995 Perfection Learning Corporation

Optional Spelling and Vocabulary Lists

Here are six word lists from the book. The words can be used as spelling or vocabulary words.

Chapters 1-3

swamp	peninsula
wilderness	island
mound	cob
marshes	intruder
range	idyllic
diary	remote
cygnets	preening
rasping	ammunition
vixen	paddled
bulrushes	creature

Chapters 4-7

glide	odious
downy	valley
vain	waterfowl
vile	altitude
aloft	frenzy
burble	communicate
defective	warden
endearments	compliment
intelligent	solitary
fate	catastrophe

Chapters 8-10

grain	crime
resonant	honor
conversation	sacrifice
coy	deplorable
attention	counselor
antics	reveille
devices	taps
fleeting	instrument
continent	peaks
quest	valleys

Chapters 11-13

cottages	sprinted
director	ovation
salary	medal
wallop	valves
prejudices	tendency
backflip	surgery
serene	composed
waddle	impersonal
blundering	plumage
canoe	moneybag

Chapters 14-17

stroll	popularity
passengers	telegram
debt	farewell
entertain	appointment
kidnapped	pinioned
celebrity	customers
lice	employer
autograph	gale
watercress	exhaustion
expensive	acquaintance

Chapters 18-21

fate	homecoming
talented	inconvenience
responsibility	mission
amputated	custody
donate	oxygen
storehouse	superficial
rucksack	escorted
proposal	kerosene
captivity	stillness
honorable	inhabit

Supplementary Activities

Below is a list of ideas that could be used as supplementary or culminating activities.

I. Oral reading

   A. To the entire class

   B. To each other

   C. To the teacher

   D. To a tape recorder

II. Group discussions

   A. Author's writing style

   B. Ideas gained from the book

   C. Parts of the book

      1. Most important

      2. Most humorous

      3. Most saddening

      4. Most exciting

      5. Most liked

   D. Characters

      1. Did the characters seem real?

      2. What did you like best about each character?

      3. What did you dislike most about each character?

      4. Which character was the student's favorite? Why?

      5. List questions to ask each character.

(continued)

Supplementary Activities

   III. Spelling bee using words from the book

   IV. Role play situations from the book

    V. Artistic creations

      A. Murals

      B. Dioramas

      C. Book jackets

      D. Posters

      E. Puppets

      F. Poetry

      G. Costumes

      H. Portraits

       I. Mobiles

      J. Songs

      K. Newspaper headlines, articles, and drawings

  VI. Research

      A. Trumpeter swans

      B. Zoos

      C. Famous trumpet players

      D. Red Rock Lakes, Montana

      E. Bird migration

 VII. Read other books by the same author

Response Key

WORD ATTACK SKILLS

Using Short Vowels (page 7)
1. boggy; 2. wilderness; 3. trudged; 4. sizzling; 5. muskrat; 6. intention; 7. problem;
8. investigated; 9. pleasant; 10. trumpeting

Finding Base Words (page 8)
1. swamp; 2. bog; 3. certain; 4. crazy; 5. discover; 6. patch; 7. warm; 8. bury; 9. trumpet;
10. rear; 11. circle; 12. reply; 13. sand; 14. step; 15. nice; 16. web; 17. slow; 18. grass;
19. scoop; 20. cry

Listening for Syllables (page 9)
1. 3; 2. 2; 3. 3; 4. 3; 5. 2; 6. 3; 7. 2; 8. 2; 9. 1; 10. 3; 11. 3; 12. 2; 13. 2; 14. 3; 15. 3; 16. 1;
17. 3; 18. 2; 19. 2; 20. 3; 21. 3; 22. 2; 23. 3; 24. 1; 25. 3; 26. 2; 27. 2; 28. 1; 29. 2; 30. 1

Making Compounds (page 10)
1. highway; 2. spellbound; 3. masterpiece; 4. blackbirds; 5. afternoon; 6. underwater;
7. another; 8. notebook; 9. sunlight; 10. shoelace

Using Long Vowels (page 12)
1. gazed; 2. behaving; 3. creatures; 4. female; 5. glided; 6. grateful; 7. triumph; 8. slight;
9. breathe; 10. file

Adding Endings (page 13)
1. watched; 2. proudly; 3. tossing; 4. gladness; 5. healthy; 6. cautiously; 7. larger;
8. thrusting; 9. daring; 10. mouthful

COMPREHENSION SKILLS

Classifying Word Groups (page 14)
1. how; 2. where; 3. how; 4. when; 5. when; 6. when; 7. where; 8. how; 9. when;
10. how; 11. how; 12. when; 13. when; 14. when; 15. where; 16. where; 17. how;
18. where; 19. where; 20. when

Matching Synonyms (page 16)
1. smart; 2. upset; 3. without; 4. meeting; 5. ordered; 6. forces; 7. place; 8. show;
9. noise; 10. feeling

Remembering Details (page 17)

1. Louis wanted to go to school with Sam and learn to read and write. 2. Louis was afraid someone would shoot him. 3. Louis untied Sam's shoelace, just as he had done the first time he met Sam. 4. Mr. Beaver wanted to be sure it was OK for Sam to keep the young swan. 5. Mrs. Beaver was afraid Louis would mess up the bedroom. 6. She called out names until she said "Louis" and the swan began to jump up and down. 7. She wanted to see what Louis was able to do.

Determining Fact and Opinion (page 18)

1. F; 2. O; 3. O; 4. O; 5. F; 6. O; 7. F; 8. F; 9. O; 10. F

Matching Antonyms (page 19)

1. success; 2. presence; 3. perfect; 4. happily; 5. male; 6. lot; 7. weak; 8. typical; 9. left; 10. elderly

Evaluating What You Read (page 20)

Responses will vary.

Determining Cause and Effect (page 21)

Set 1: 2; 5; 3; 1; 4
Set 2: 3; 1; 2; 5; 4

Remembering Details (page 22)

1. Louis looked different than the rest of the cygnets. 2. It was hard to fly with things hanging around his neck. 3. Louis knew that Sam could help him with his problems. 4. Sam bought a music book and read the instructions to Louis. 5. Louis played the trumpet in the morning, at mealtimes, and at bedtime. 6. Louis was going to be paid $100 for the season. 7. Mr. Brickle said camps need strange names so they sound interesting.

Discovering Meaning Through Context (page 23)

1. belongings; 2. grew dim; 3. back; 4. touched shore; 5. squashed; 6. begged; 7. hit; 8. end; 9. strange; 10. stay

Using Cloze Reading (page 25)

1. trumpet; 2. noise; 3. positions; 4. cheeks; 5. tongue; 6. trying; 7. clear; 8. beat; 9. listen; 10. trumpeter; 11. summer

Getting the Main Idea (page 26)

a. Louis was good at volleyball. b. Louis saved Applegate from drowning. c. Louis wanted his web slit so he could play all kinds of music. d. Louis needed all of his possessions.

Sequencing Events (page 28)

Set 1: 1; 4; 3; 5; 2
Set 2: 2; 4; 1; 5; 3

Classifying Words (page 29)

1. Serena/places where Louis spent time; 2. watercress/bodies of water;
3. double/numbers; 4. boat/things Louis wore around his neck; 5. garden/buildings;
6. tickets/kinds of furniture; 7. squirrels/kinds of birds; 8. napkin/silverware; 9.
desk/things usually found in a bathroom; 10. boatman/workers in the Ritz Hotel

Making Inferences (page 31)

a. 3; b. 1; c. 1; d. 2; e. 2

STUDY SKILLS

Choosing Correct Meanings (page 33)

1. 1; 2. 2; 3. 3; 4. 3; 5. 2; 6. 3; 7. 2; 8. 2; 9. 2; 10. 1; 11. 1; 12. 1; 13. 3; 14. 1; 15. 1

Making an Outline (page 35)

Trumpeter Swans

I. Characteristics of swans	II. Characteristics of trumpeter swans	III. Swan families
A. Water birds	A. Found in North America	A. Strong family ties
B. Flattened bills	B. Trumpet-like call	B. Mate for life
C. Long necks and wings	C. All white feathers	C. Babies called *cygnets*
D. Water-repellent feathers	D. Largest swan	D. Cygnets stay with parents
E. Short tails and legs		

Using Guide Words (page 37)

able—hid	**hide—plain**	**plate—wrote**
1. afternoons	1. honor	1. played
2. concerts	2. hope	2. public
3. duck	3. lake	3. rifle
4. farewell	4. passengers	4. shiny
5. hauled	5. ping	5. sweet
6. heart	6. place	6. works

Using a Pronunciation Key (page 38)

1. accident; 2. pinioned; 3. breeze; 4. poem; 5. vanished; 6. attack; 7. buildings; 8. pain;
9. valuable; 10. civilization; 11. amputated; 12. premiums; 13. cygnets; 14. bayou

Determining Alphabetical Order (page 39)

A. 1; 6; 3; 4; 2; 5
B. 4; 1; 2; 6; 5; 3
C. 6; 2; 5; 3; 4; 1
D. 4; 5; 2; 1; 6; 3
E. 1; 6; 3; 2; 5; 4
F. 5; 6; 2; 3; 1; 4
G. 1; 5; 2; 4; 3; 6
H. 3; 5; 1; 2; 6; 4

CREATIVE SKILLS

Using Descriptive Words (page 40)
Responses will vary.

Recalling an Event (page 41)
Responses will vary.

Writing a Journal Sample (page 42)
Responses will vary.

Creating a Character (page 43)
Responses will vary.

Writing a Book Recommendation (page 44)
Responses will vary.

Explaining Feelings (page 45)
Responses will vary.